# CONNECT THE DOTS
# AGES 4-8

## By: Activity Nest
*activitynest.org*

This book is dedicated to the children of the world. May your hearts be full of joy.

If you enjoy the book, please consider leaving a review wherever you bought it.

**ISBN:** 978-1-951791-10-0

# Get All Our New Releases For FREE!

Sign up to our VIP Newsletter to get all of our

future releases absolutely free!

www.activitynest.org/free

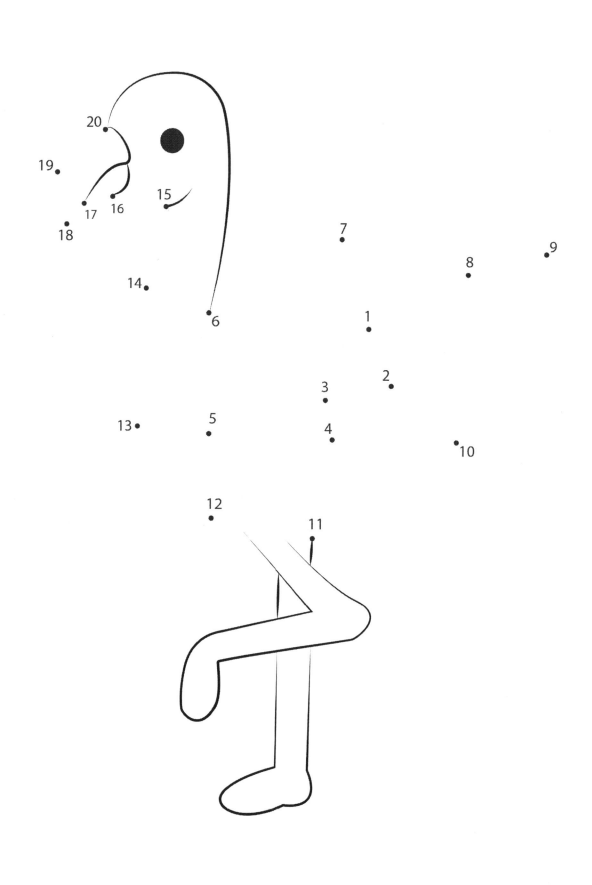

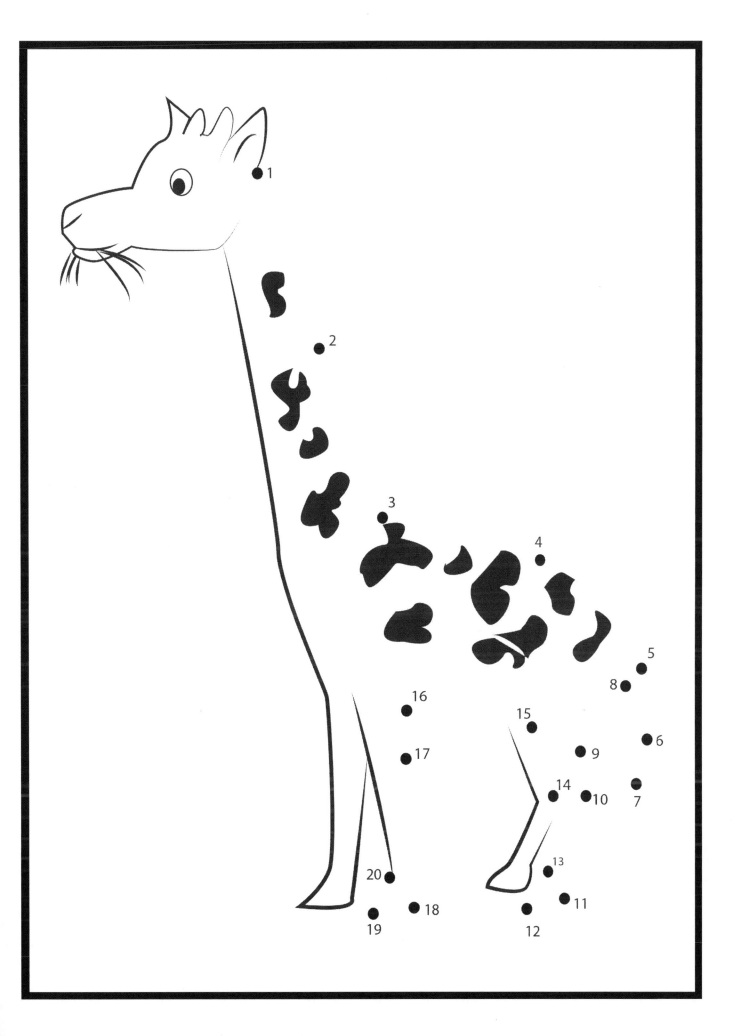

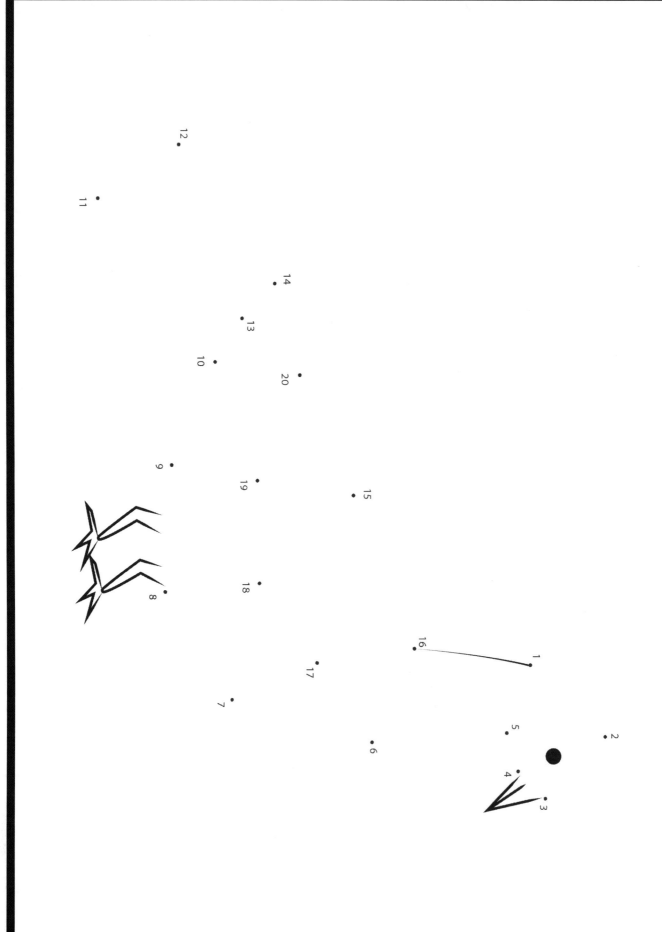

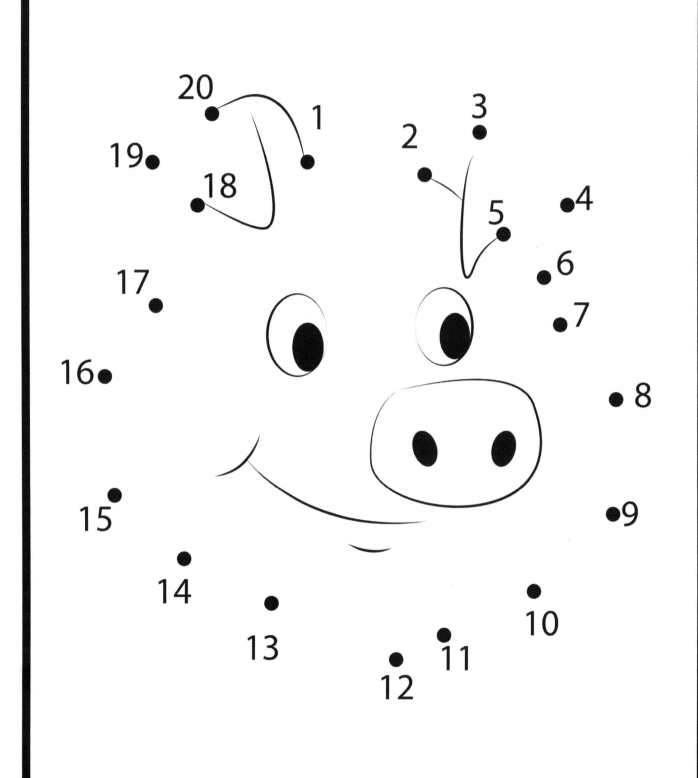

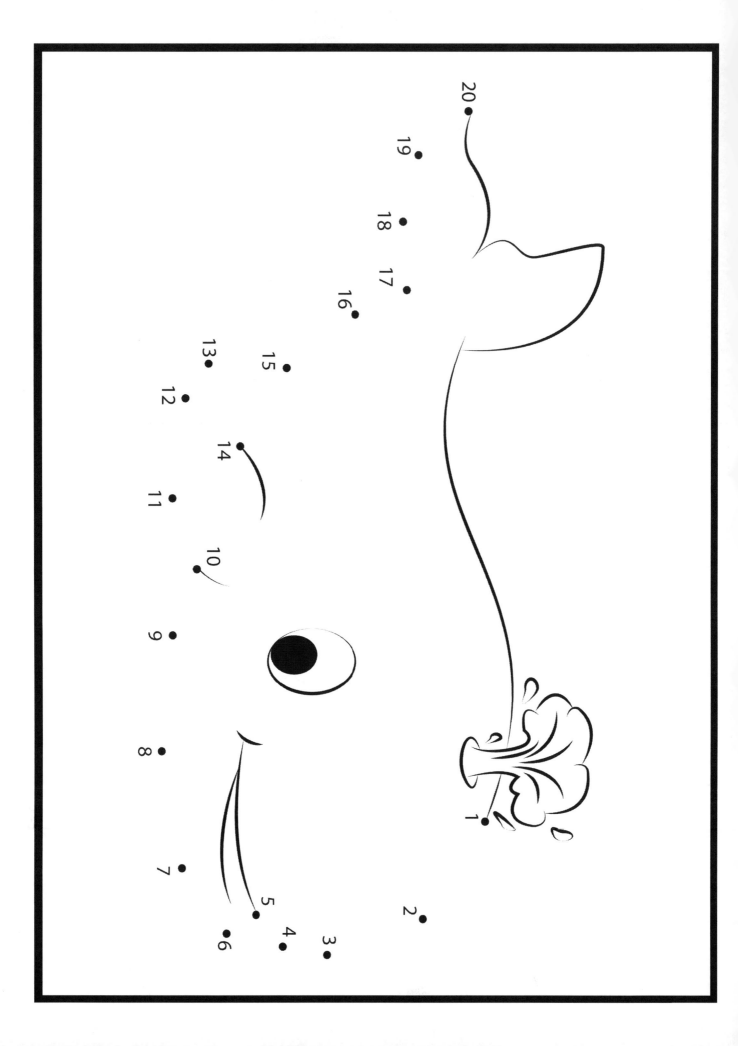

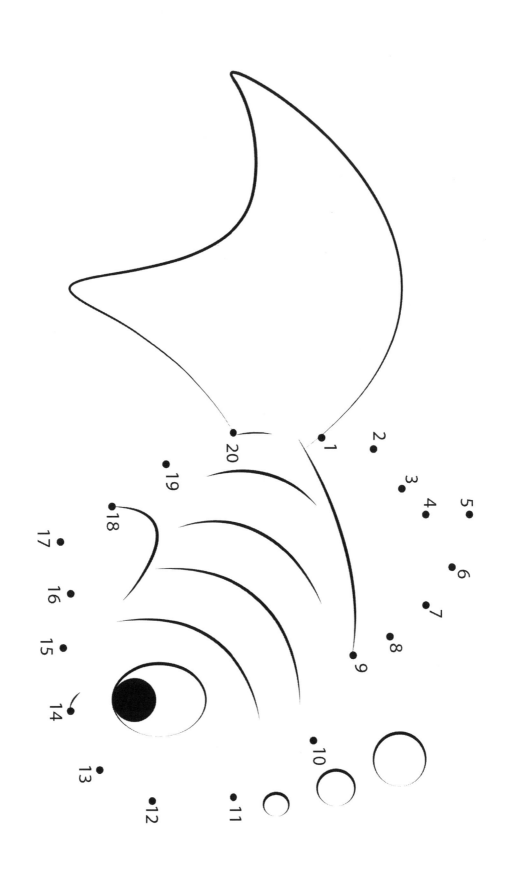

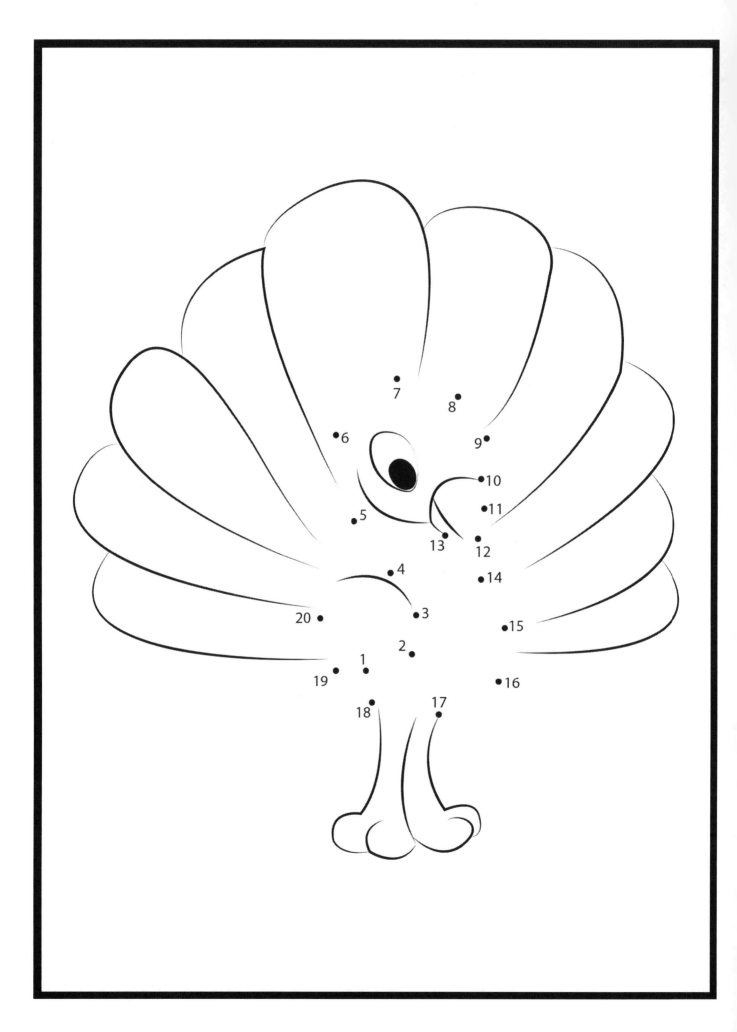

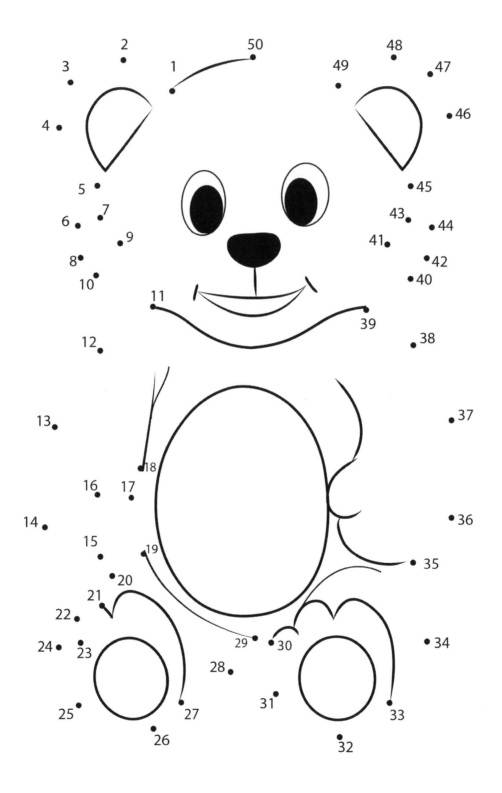

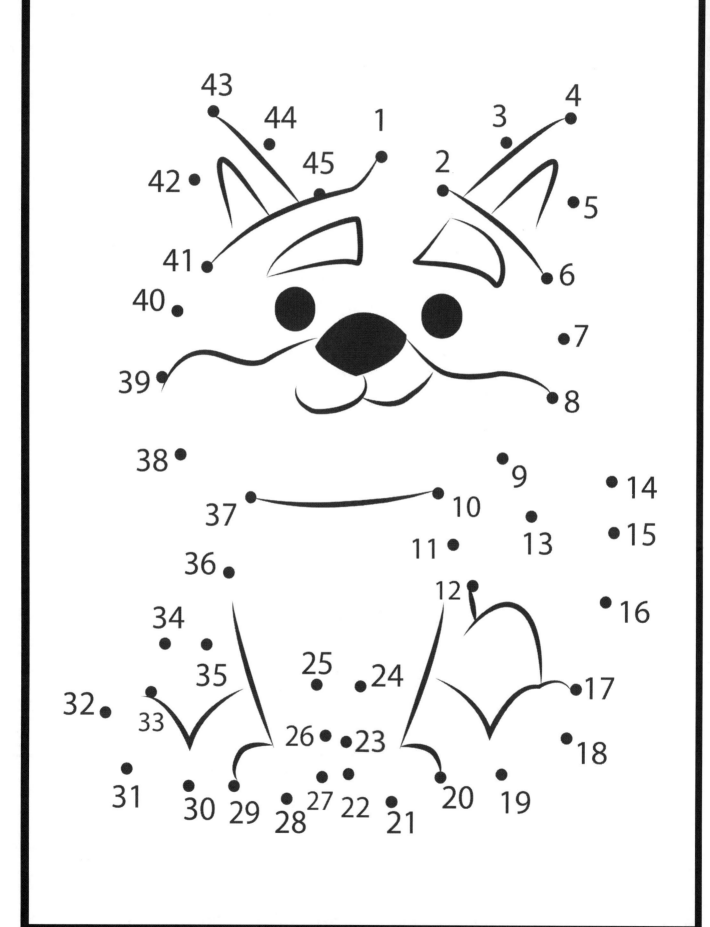

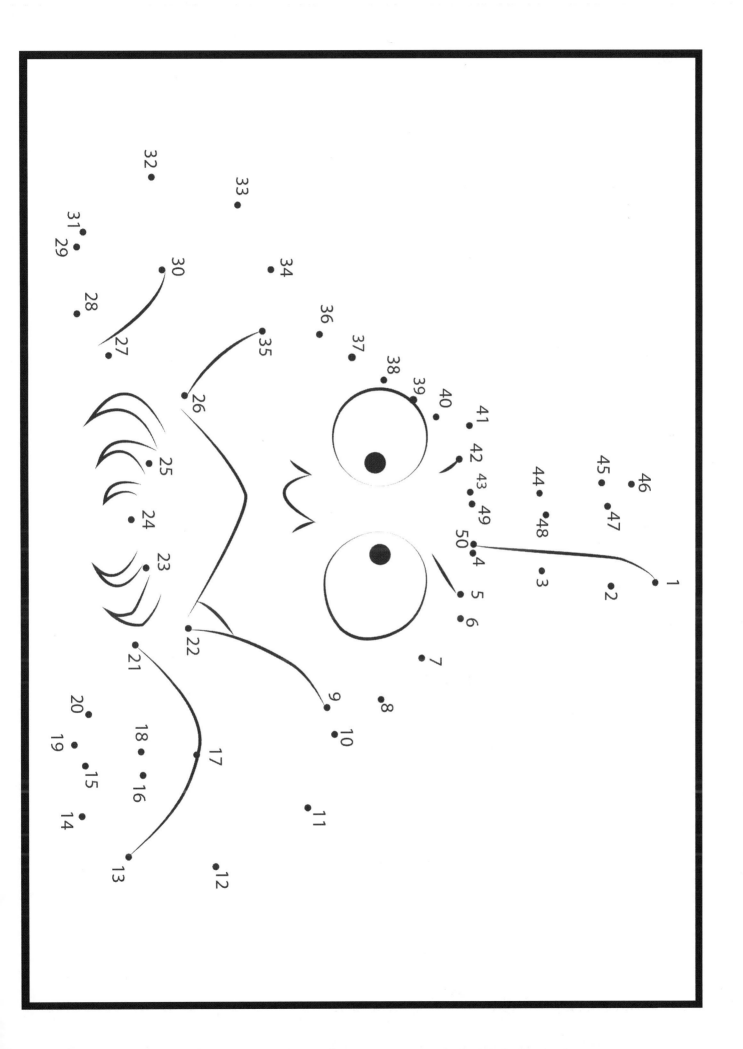

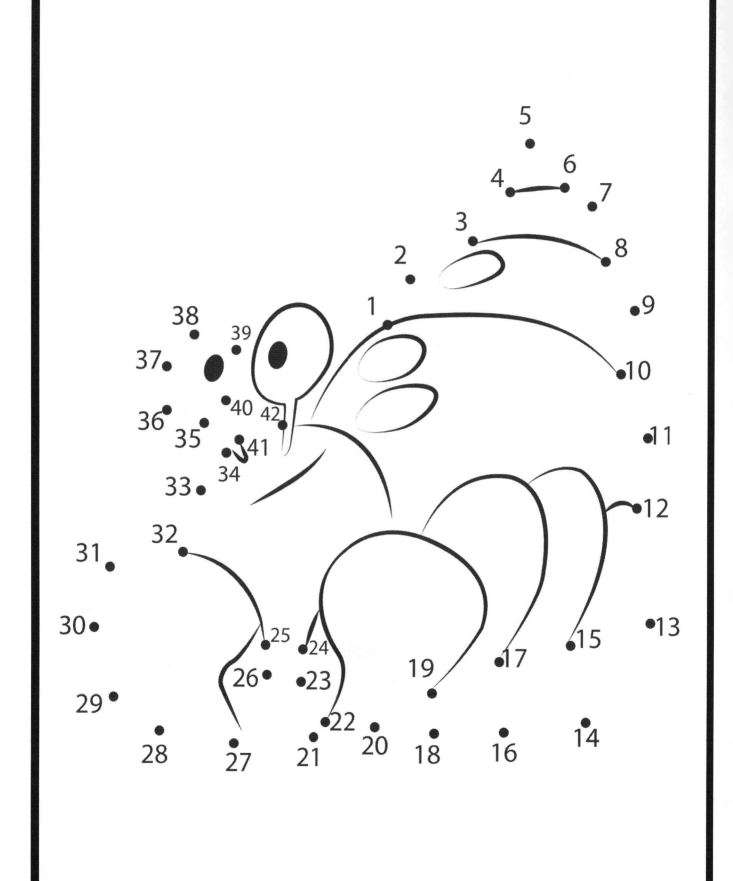

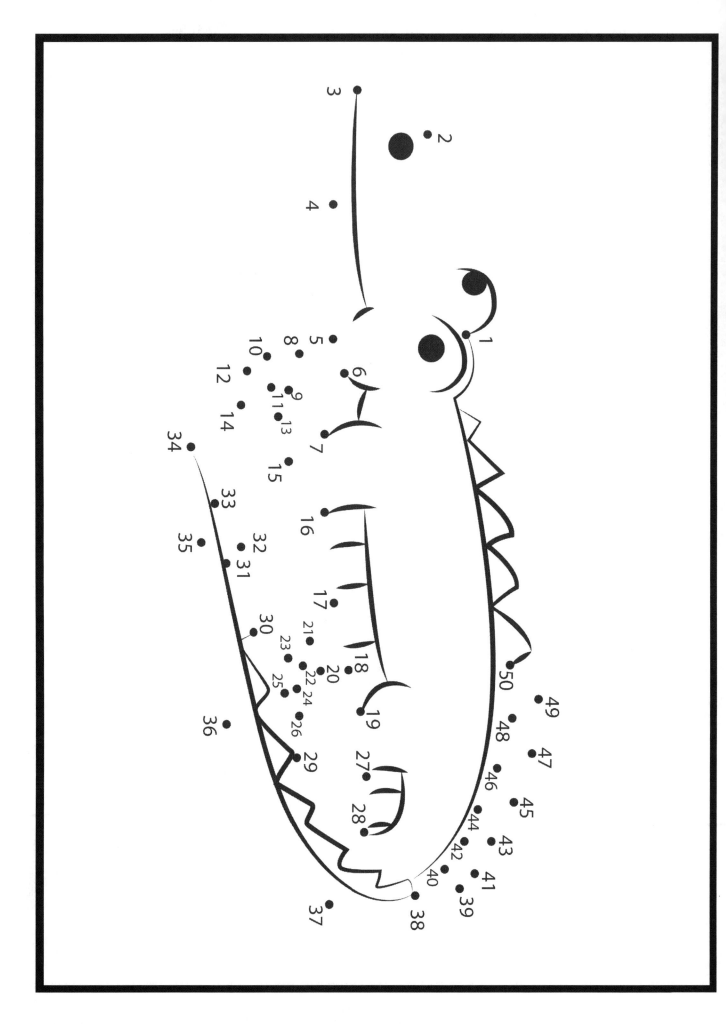

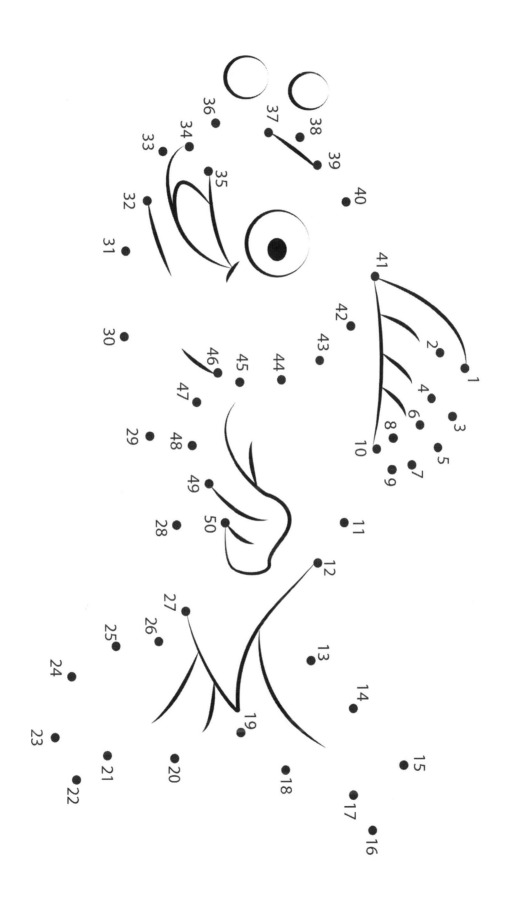

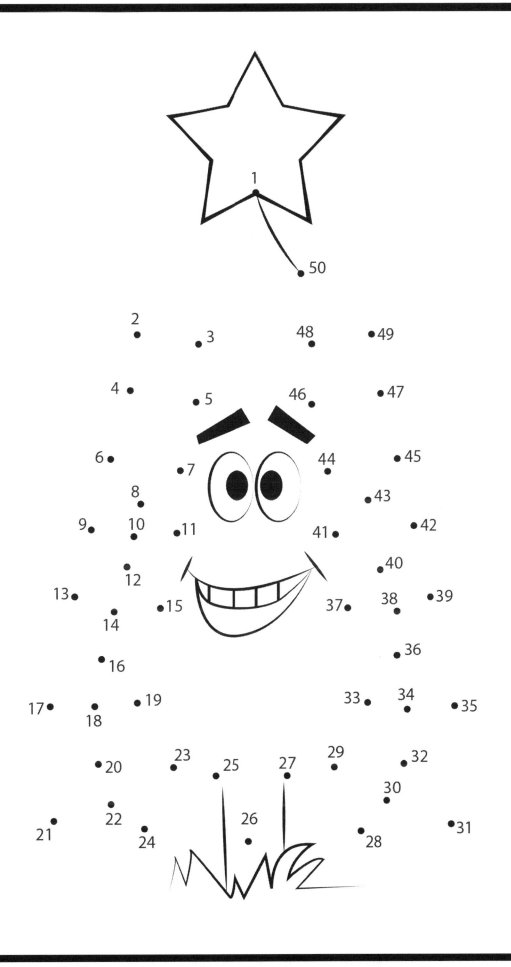

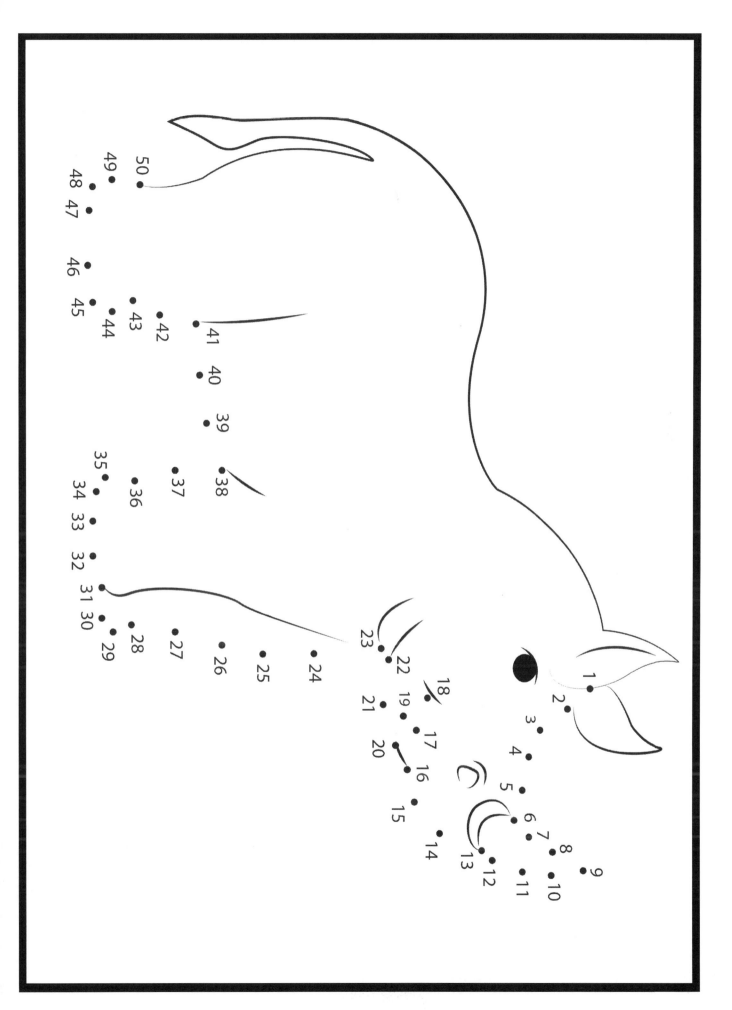

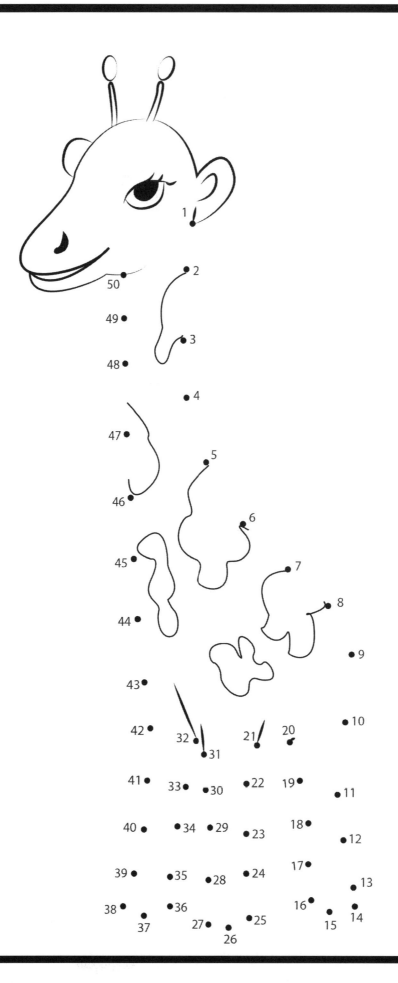

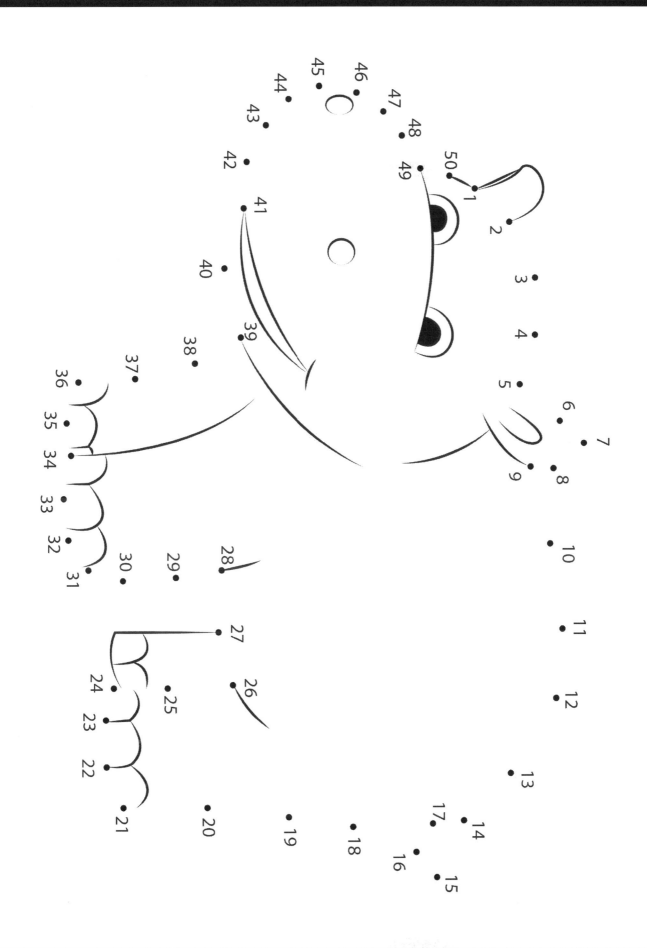

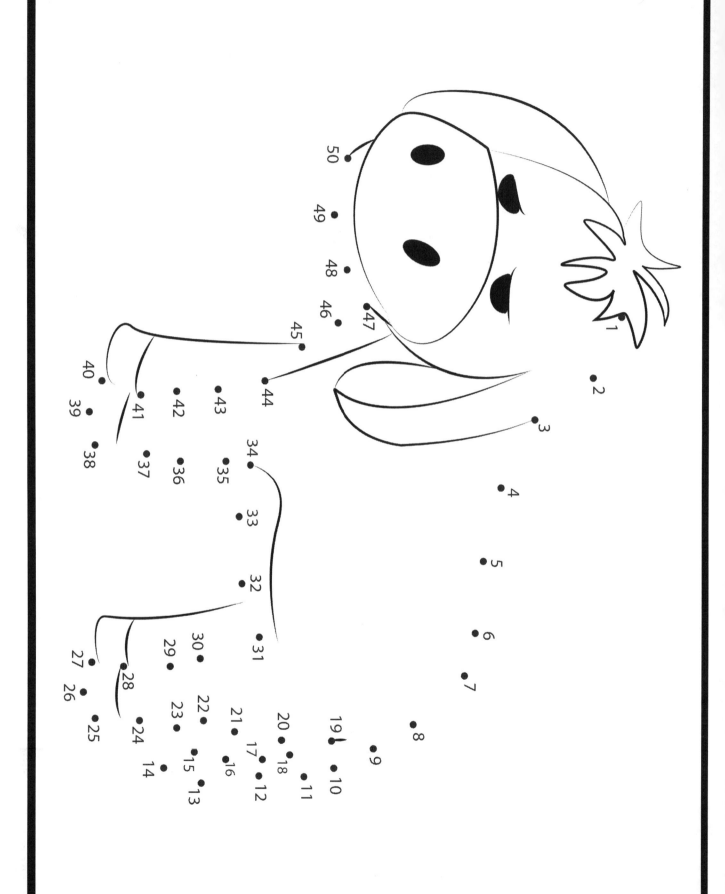

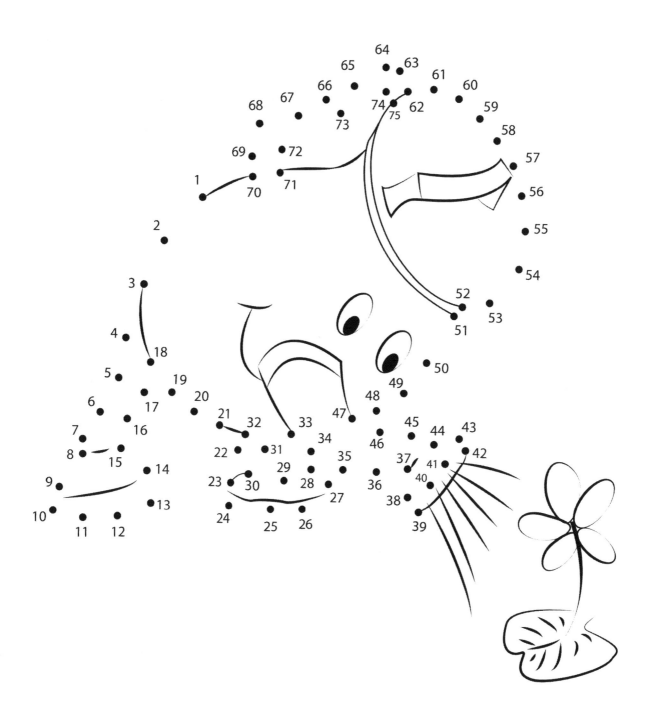

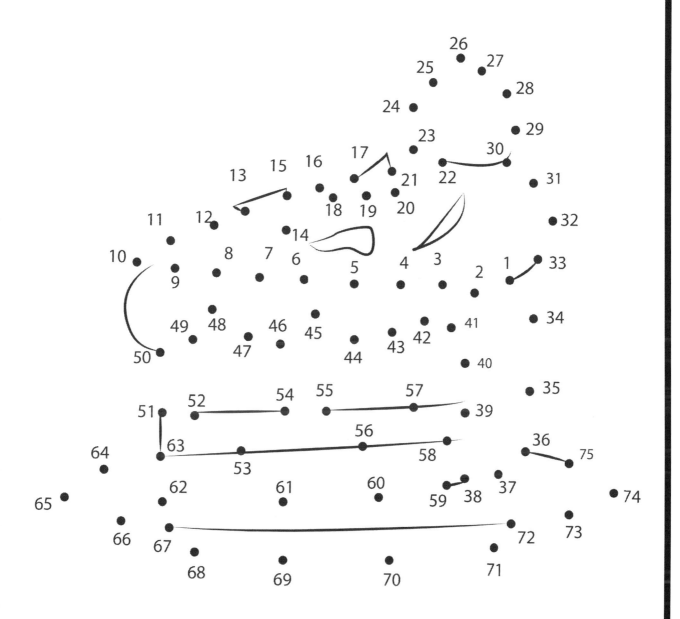

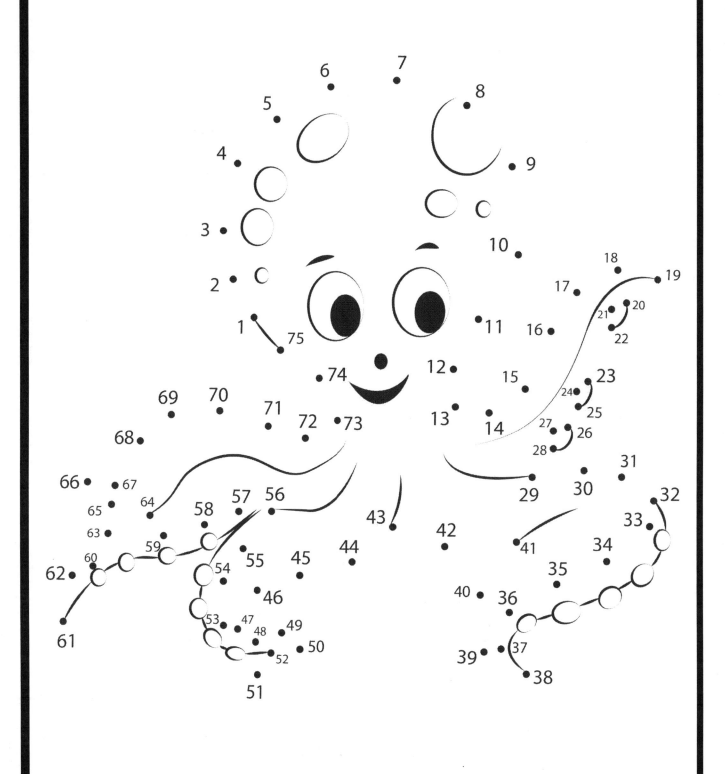

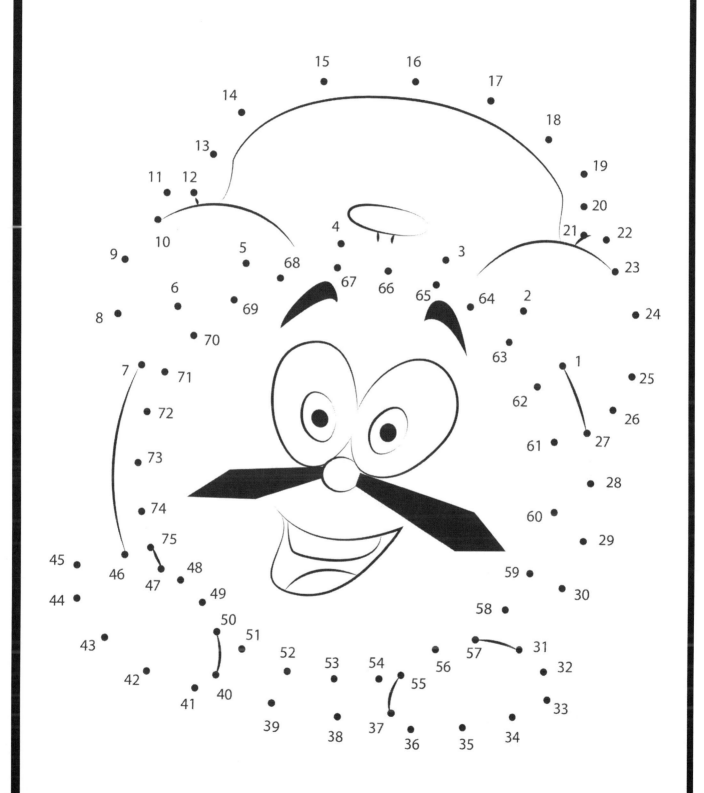

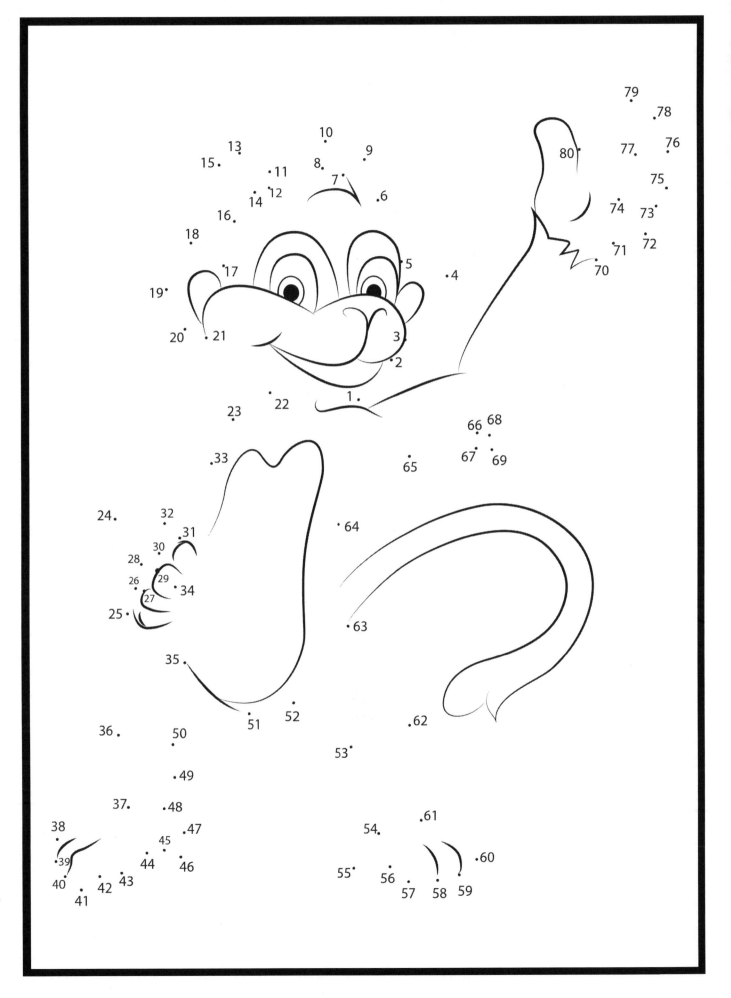

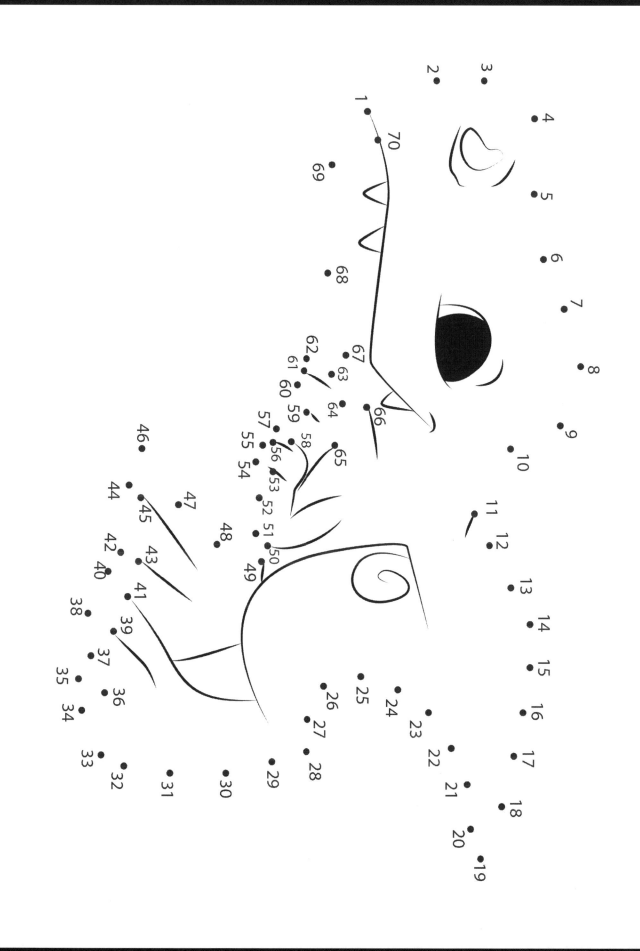

# ANSWERS

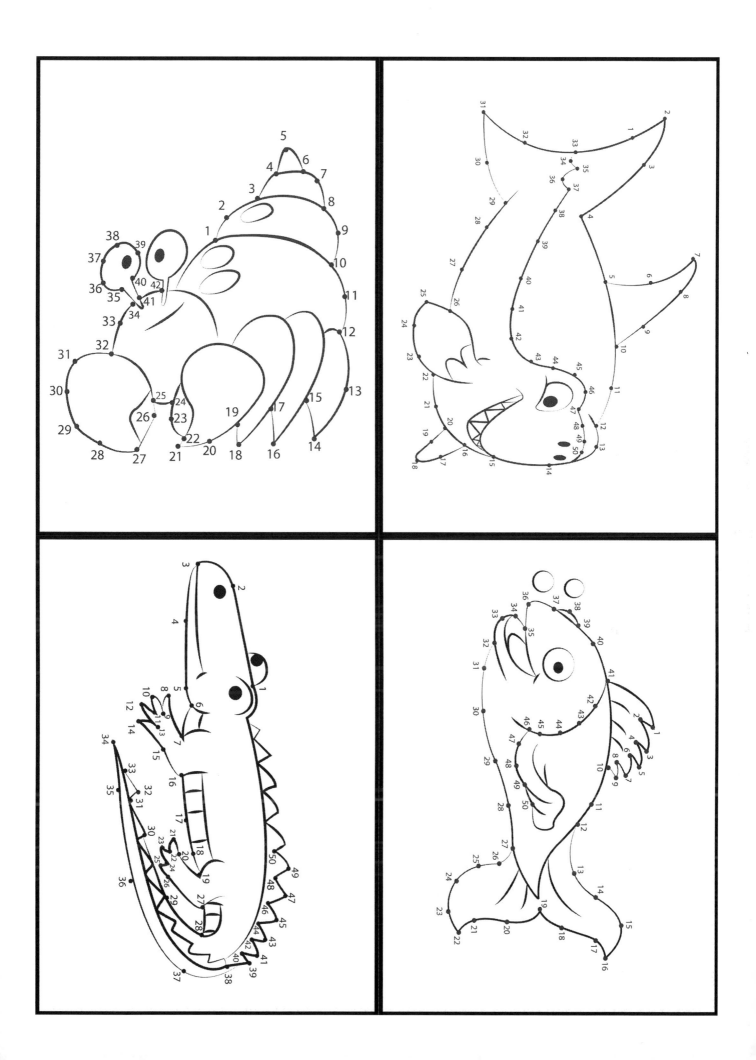

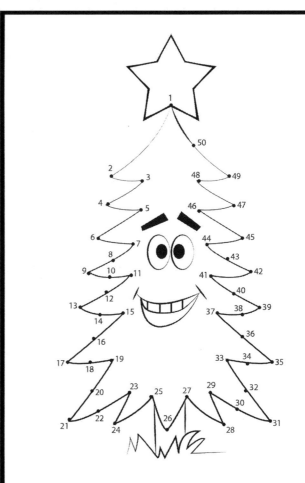

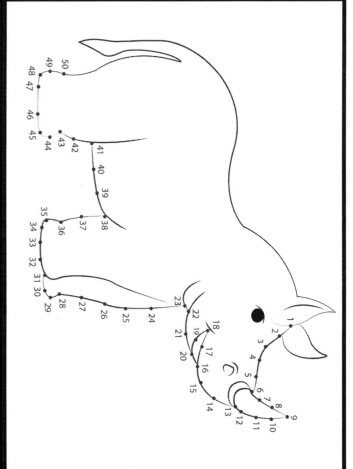

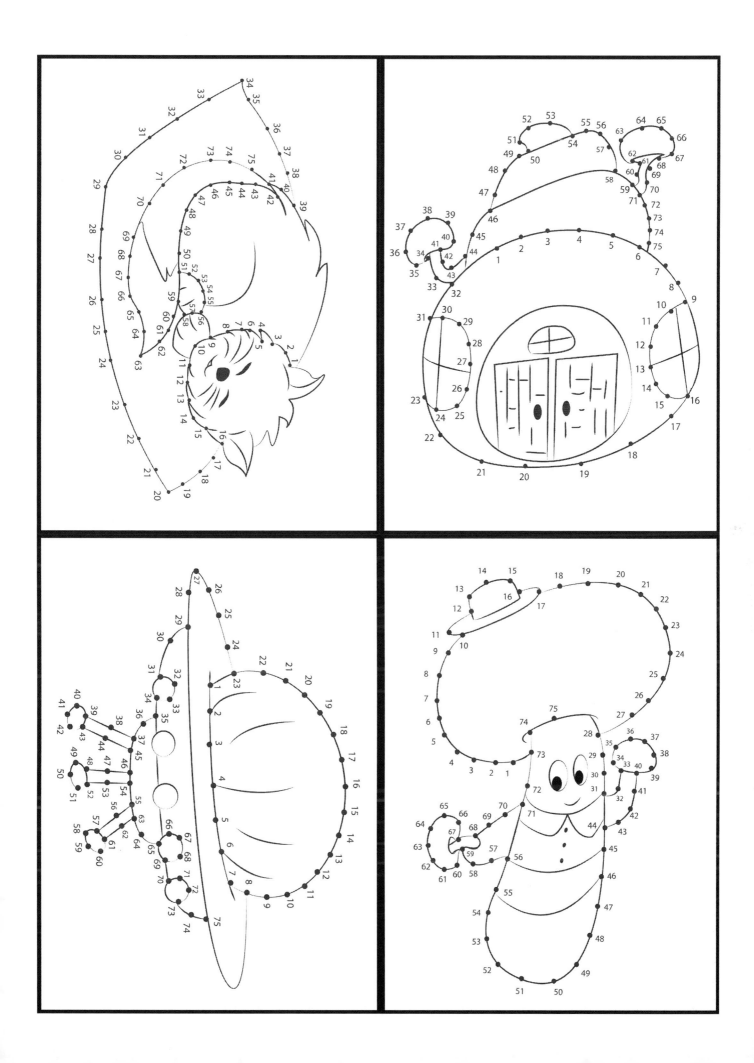

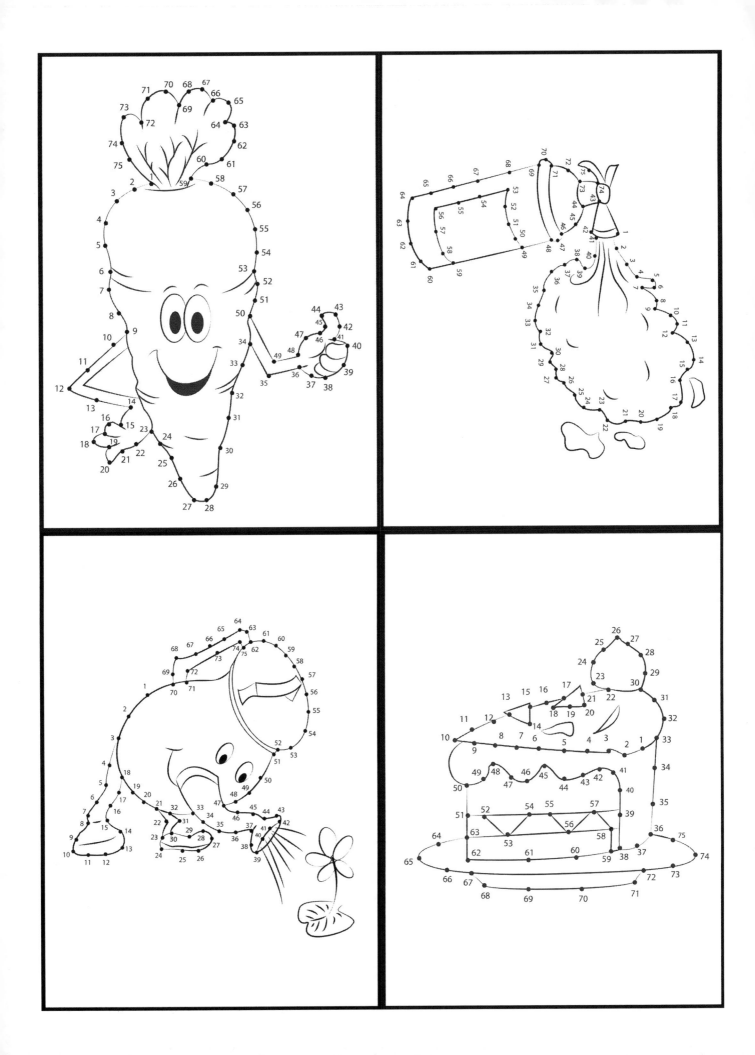

# THANK YOU!

## Please leave us a review on Amazon.

Amazon reviews are very important to our business and
help other activity lovers find our books.

Please go to this book on Amazon and let us know your
honest opinion.

It would mean the world to us. Thank you!

Don't forget to sign up to our VIP Newsletter to get all of
our future releases absolutely free!

www.activitynest.org/free

Made in the USA
Columbia, SC
16 March 2021